# Puppies
## in the
## Snow

For Annie-Leigh

ISBN 0-439-44906-5

12 11 10 9                                        5 6 7 8/0

Printed in the U.S.A.
First printing, January 2003

# Puppies
## in the
# Snow

## by James Young

SCHOLASTIC INC.

New York　Toronto　London　Auckland　Sydney
Mexico City　New Delhi　Hong Kong　Buenos Aires

**One** lonely puppy in the snow,
so far from home, so far to go!

Only the big black crow as she flew
saw him go by —
and then there were . . .

**Two** friendly puppies in the snow,
so far from home, so far to go!

Only the owl in her hollow tree
saw them go by —
and then there were . . .

**Three** funny puppies in the snow,
so far from home, so far to go!

Only the cat at the cabin door
saw them go by —
and then there were . . .

**Four** busy puppies in the snow,
so far from home, so far to go!

Only the bees in their warm little hive
saw them go by —
and then there were . . .

**Five** fast puppies in the snow,
so far from home, so far to go!

Only the squirrel in her nest of sticks
saw them go by —
and then there were . . .

**Six** sliding puppies in the snow,
so far from home, so far to go!

Only the hawk high in the heavens
saw them go by —
and then there were . . .

**Seven** jumping puppies in the snow,
so far from home, so far to go!

Only the horse at the barnyard gate
saw them go by —
and then there were . . .

**Eight** frisky puppies in the snow,
so far from home, so far to go!

Only the possum that hung from the pine
saw them go by —
and then there were . . .

**Nine** clever puppies in the snow,
so far from home, so far to go!

Only the bear in her deep, dark den
saw them go by —
and then there were . . .

**Ten** hungry puppies in the snow!
Almost home, somehow they know.

Their mother is waiting.
She counts each head.
Then she feeds them and warms them
and puts them to bed.

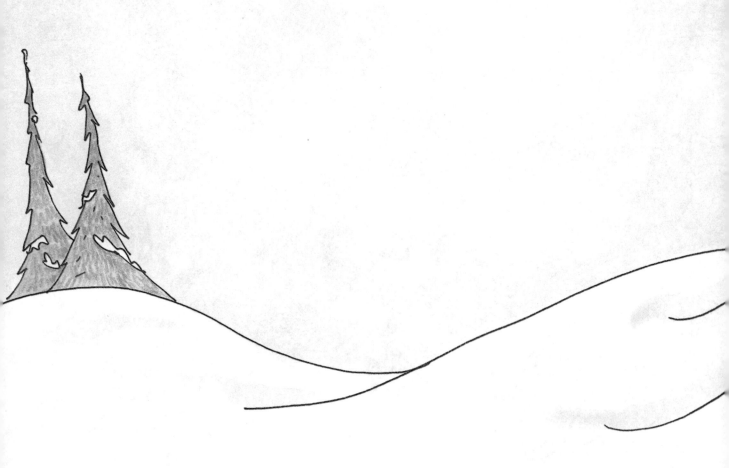